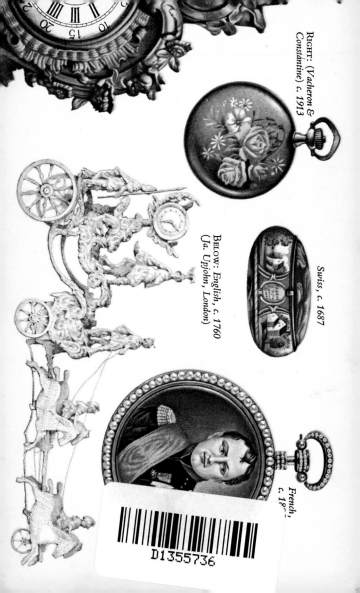

RIGHT: (*Vacheron & Constantine, c. 1913*)

Swiss, c. 1687

BELOW: English, *c. 1760* (*Ja. Upjohn, London*)

French, c. 18—

D1355736

ABOUT THE COVER:

Examples from the golden age of watchmaking—1600 to 1800. The scene enamelled on the lid of the watch at centre shows Cleopatra reaching for the deadly asp smuggled past the Roman guards in a basket of figs by the faithful Charmian

ACKNOWLEDGEMENT: *The photograph on page 6: Art Reference Bureau, courtesy La Bibliotheque Nationale de Belgique*

PUBLISHED BY
PAUL HAMLYN LIMITED • Westbook House • Fulham Broadway • London

CLOCKS AND WATCHES

BY CHESTER JOHNSON

ILLUSTRATED BY HARRY McNAUGHT

PAUL HAMLYN · LONDON

CLOCK TIME is still something new—although timetelling has been a "science" for some 4,000 years. Prehistoric, prescientific man, shivering in his cave, baking in interglacial summers, knew almost nothing of time—but he sensed it in the rhythms of sun, moon, and stars, the turns of tides and seasons, the beat of his heart, the hungry periods from one meal to the next. Perhaps he measured it from mammoth to mammoth. ■ Timetelling began when planting, herding man first read meaning into

This huge Indian sundial is the largest in the world. It is in a park of monumental dials built about 1724 by Jai Singh, Maharaja of Jaipur—a gifted mathematician and astronomer. The staircase points at the polestar and casts its shadow on the curved hour scale below

the movement of the heavens. Agricultural man had to know the yearly phases with an accuracy never needed by his unsettled ancestors. The Egyptians, correlating the annual rising of the brightest star Sirius with the Nile flood, invented the oldest calendar we have. Stonehenge was probably both a temple and calendar dial to Stone and Bronze Age Britons; midsummer sunrise and midwinter sunset in relation to four of the biggest stones could have high-lighted summer and winter solstices to a sun-worshiping people. ■ Our dating system is still based on the earth's yearly journey round the sun, but our time sense is no longer so sun-oriented. Sidereal—the astronomer's—time is based on the "rotation" of the stars. Even solar—our 24-hour—time is no longer pivoted on high noon but based on "high" midnight at Greenwich, England—where, in the eyes of horologists (those technologists of time), the sun is always set. Hourly timetelling was probably invented by settled, sun-watching peoples who felt the need to regulate their day as precisely as they had the agricultural year. Timetelling began a technological revolution; we are its direct heirs. ■ Earth's daily spin was first converted to hourly time by the sundial—an instrument showing the motion of the earth by measuring the movement of the sun's shadow. Sundials—possibly invented first by the sun-

The shadow-casting bar faced east in the morning, west in the afternoon. The 12 hours of daylight (longer in summer) were indicated by the edge of the shadow on the ruled base

Oldest known sundial (Egyptian, c. 1450 b.c.)

Egyptian astronomers taking a "fix" on the polestar with sighting stick and plumb lines. Two marks in the sand, with a line between, pointed north and south. The method was invaluable for positioning more advanced dials—or pyramids

TOP RIGHT: *A Mixtec priest of ancient Mexico observing a star's position through the notch made by two crossed sticks. The ancient Maya probably used similar techniques in developing their phenomenally accurate calendar. Primitive astronomers in both the Old World and the New World measured the movement of the heavens and noted the all-important cycles of agricultural time.*

BOTTOM RIGHT: *Romans and Greeks in the time of Caesar had over a dozen different kinds of sundials. In the one shown here, a sweeping shaft of light, shining through the pierced bronze plate at the top, spotlighted the 12 daylight hours and the four seasons engraved on the surface of the hemispherical hollow*

ABOVE: From *Codex Nuttall* (c. 1400)

drenched Sumerians around 5,000 years ago—spread throughout the ancient world. Egyptians, Greeks, Romans, men of medieval Islam and of the Renaissance, and later dialists gradually developed the sundial from a stick stuck in the ground (still used by the head-hunting Dyaks of Borneo) to a scientific, often beautifully decorated instrument capable of showing time to the minute by either sun, moon, or stars; the date, including feast days; sunrise and set; angle of the sun; and signs of the zodiac. Such was the accuracy of some

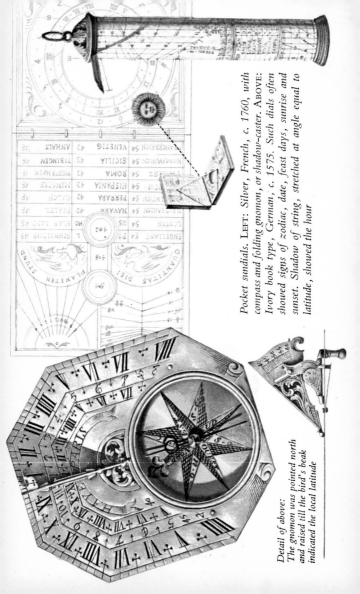

Pocket sundials. Left: Silver, French, c. 1760, with compass and folding gnomon, or shadow-caster. Above: Ivory book type, German, c. 1575. Such dials often showed signs of zodiac, date, feast days, sunrise and sunset. Shadow of string, stretched at angle equal to latitude, showed the hour

Detail of above:
The gnomon was pointed north and raised till the bird's beak indicated the local latitude

ENGKREICH 54	VENETIG 54	ANHALT 36
KOMANIEN 54	SICILIA 54	TIBINGEN 48
THIREISZ 54	ROMA 54	WESTERHAIN 48
PRE... 54	HISPANIA 54	MINSTER 48
...NDR 54	FERRARA 42	GILCH 48
BEHAMEN 54	NAVARR 42	PLANER 48
LENTEN 54	US 40	ELAG LAND 48
ENGELLANT 54	PO 7	SCHWIRZMOR 48

QUANTITAS DIEI

PLANETEN STUND

dials that it was only in 1900 that French railwaymen stopped setting their watches by the sun. Clock time (an average of solar time) and sundial time agree only four times a year, but sundial time can be converted to clock-time by simple corrections. For this reason, and because they were simpler, more compact, and cheaper, sundials competed successfully with clocks and watches until almost 1800. ■ "A thing measured", said the Romans, "is never lost"—except time itself. The sundial's sunless competitors were designed to do just this: to lose water, sand, burning wax, or oil at a regular, measurable rate. The earliest of these, perhaps as old as the sundial, was the water

clock, the first timekeeper using moving parts —in the simplest types only the water level itself, but in the most complex an ingenious system of floats, cogwheels, dials, and pointers. The Greeks called them clepsydras (water-stealers) and built probably the world's largest in Athens to "standardize" the city's time. Named the Tower of the Winds, it still stands today. ■ The Romans, calling them "night clocks", used them in law courts to "prevent babbling", according to one ancient writer; but the water clock keepers could be bribed to cheat on the water supply, allowing lawyers to drone past their allotted time or to "cut their opponent's water". Caesar found to his surprise that the "barbarian" Britons had water clocks— and even used one of theirs to prove that their summer nights were indeed shorter than those in Italy. ■ Clepsydras tapped technological skills unused in the ancient slave-powered econ-

RIGHT: *Armillary sphere (c. 1600),*
one of the most advanced astronomical-
astrological instruments of pre-telescope
days. Usually a foot or two in diameter.
The bronze circles were adjusted to show
positions of stars and planets, plot horo-
scopes, show sun time by a shadow or
bright spot. FAR RIGHT, ABOVE: *A Spanish*
noonday gun, c. 1650. A signal to set
clocks by, the gun fired when sun focused
on the touchhole. BELOW: *A collector's*
prize. Set level and north by built-in
plumb bob and compass, this elaborate
dial showed both minutes and hours.
German, c. 1750

Chinese folding
finger ring dial,
with compass
underneath,
c. 1800

12

omies. They became mechanical marvels employing carefully hand-cut cogwheels, often of bronze, ebony, or ivory; cylinder-dials rotated against moving pointers to show the unequal winter and summer hours. A few could even strike—by bells, whistles, or organ pipes. The tubing was sometimes of gold to prevent corrosion, and the flow-holes of perforated gems (the first jewelled bearings) to prevent wear from affecting the drip-rate. ■ Harun-al Rashid, Caliph of Baghdad, impressed Charlemagne by sending a large, elaborate water clock calculated to inspire Frankish courtiers with awe at Islam. This clock made an hourly spectacle of itself by dropping metal balls on a bass

BELOW: *Reproduction of Roman water clock of about 50 B.C.*

RIGHT BACKGROUND: *As water syphoned from the float tank (A), the sinking figure (B) pointed to the day/night hours on the drum (C), which—turned by weight of syphoned water in the wheel (D)—showed the changing lengths of day and night*

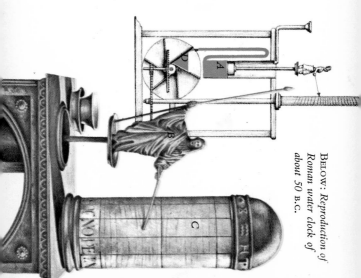

drum from 12 small doors, closed at 12 o'clock by a dozen automaton horsemen. ■ Water clocks dripped on through the ages until the later 1700s; they, too, like the sundial, were cheaper than clocks, but most were not spill-proof and all were inaccurate. Simpler, more compact timekeepers were not forthcoming, however, until sandglasses, candle clocks, and lamp clocks appeared. Sandglasses may have been used to time night watches by the Roman armies. By the early 1300s "hour" glasses—most ran for less—had become fairly common although they were, when richly decorated, still very acceptable gifts to princes and prelates. Sandglasses were used by the Holy Inquisition to measure periods of torture meted out to heretics and other nonconformists. Protestant preachers used them

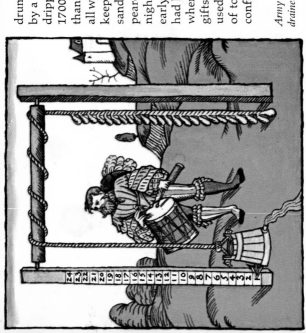

Army water clock, c. 1564. The hours were shown as water drained from the slowly rising, counterweighted bucket

Though useful at night, candle and lamp clocks were better light-givers than timekeepers. Drafts and dirty wicks made accuracy impossible

well into the 1700s to time their three- to four-hour sermons.

■ King Alfred, traditional inventor of the candle clock, grieving after almost complete defeat by the Danes, may have found comfort in the Anglo-Saxon proverb: "Time and money soothes all men's moods". Later, the Danes subdued and his reign established, he could enjoy the light shed by his candle clock, glowing gently in the gloom of Dark Age Britain. ■ Most existing lamp clocks date from the 17th and 18th centuries. Sandglasses were used on shipboard until the early 1900s in determining the ship's speed; a triangular-shaped wood "parachute" tied to a length of knotted line was thrown overside by one sailor while a second timed with a half-minute glass the number of knots swept out, converting the result into knots of speed. Some attempts were made to use sandglasses to time sea voyages; Columbus is supposed to have done so. But over long periods, even with the best hourglass-turning attendant, errors of hours crept in.

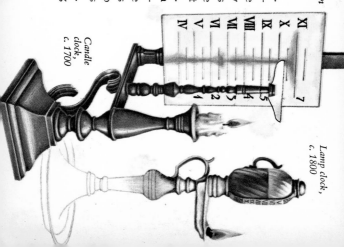

Candle clock, c. 1700

Lamp clock, c. 1800

XI
X
IX
VIII
VII
VI
V
IV

7
1
2
3
4
5

MECHANICAL CLOCKS

Timekeeping began to be noisier in the late 1200s when an alien mechanical sound interrupted the quiet flow of sundial- and water-clock-measured hours. No clocks have survived from this period, but here and there town and monastery chronicles mention a *horologium*—a familiar medieval term for timekeepers in general—in a way which hints at something quite new, the mechanical clock. We now know that cogwheels turned by the power of falling weights were known to the ancient Greeks, but so far history denies them the escapement—a feature present in every true clock which allows the control or escape wheel to turn tooth-by-tooth at regular, time-measuring intervals. Descriptions of their clockwork-like machines—an astronomical "computer" has been retrieved from a lump of coppery corrosion found by sponge divers

"Quartet" sand glass, which showed the hour and its fractions, c. 1550. It could be mounted on a hand-set "scorekeeper" for counting the number of times the glass was turned

The invention of mechanical clocks caused a revolution in timekeeping. This illustration from an illuminated manuscript (c. 1500) contains a representation of a cathedral clock and its alarm works. On the table are a variety of sundials— and a spring clock, a sign of times to come

in a ship sunk about 65 B.C.—show that the Greeks could have invented a true clock, the concept of which may have been transmitted to medieval Europe by the Islamic Arabs, the conquering inheritors of what remained of Greek and Alexandrian science. ■ It is also possible that the mechanical clock or its concept came to Europe from China, where since A.D. 130 semi-mechanical clocks are recorded. Part water, part mechanical clock, they might have been the missing link. ■ The first clocks did not *show* the time but—ponderously revolving their iron wheels, clacking their weighted foliot or regulating bar back and forth—they sounded an alarm, warning the monastery ringer to sound the canonical hours from Matins to Complin. Twenty-four-hour striking clocks—in some the dial turned—began to make themselves heard in the richer cities by 1335. Striking—frequently the job of an automaton "jack"

or "jacomart", instead of a human bellringer—and hour counting varied in practice from town to town. Time varied from clock to clock; even the best could be off by two hours a day. ■ Domestic clocks began to appear in the late 1300s in the chambers of princes, kings, and popes. Hourly striking, sometimes with quarter-hour "ting-tangs" and an alarm, co-ordinated activities of both master and servants. Later (1600-1657), "lantern" type chamber clocks used practically the same type of escapement. Setting by sundial was necessary as the clocks at best kept time to within only five to ten minutes a day. As many as four weights dangled for the cat or children to play with; once upon their hook or bracket, clocks had to stay; moving them from room to room was a nuisance. ■ The oldest spring models preserved (c. 1500) look like weightless versions of the house clock, but a more elegant clock

Timekeeping by wheels. The earliest clocks had (not including the hand) only **4 main parts**: *A weight-turned drum whose first or great wheel (A) drove, via the centre wheel (B), the escape wheel (C) through alternate, tooth-by-tooth engagements with each of the pallets (D, E) on the axle or verge (F) of the weighted regulating bar (G), the back-and-forth swinging governor or foliot. These oscillations controlled the rate of the clock by alternately stopping and releasing the escape wheel. This type of escapement was characteristic of the earlier clocks and watches. The foliot weights were moved out to slow the clock, and inward to make it go faster. Note how the small gear or pinion (1) on the axle of the weight-drum drove the hour-hand wheel (2).*

The very earliest clocks had hours marked directly on this wheel and the hand was only a fixed pointer riveted on the clock frame. The clock was wound by cranking an axle (3)

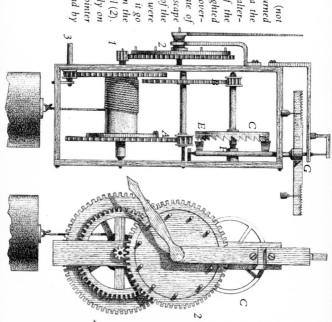

Wells Cathedral clock, c. 1450. The knights joust at hourly intervals. Date and moon phase were also often shown (as here) by such early clocks

was in demand. The old escapement—a "balance" wheel later replaced the bar or foliot—could be used, but the decreasing power of the uncoiling spring, a long ribbon of tempered steel, had first to be solved. ■ The earliest dated spring clock extant, made in 1525 for King Sigismund I of Poland, used a brass spring and, as a spring equalizer, an ingenious device (sketched by Leonardo da Vinci and used in ships' chronometers to this day) called a fusee. The (German) alternative "stackfreed" was simpler to make and allowed the clock to run longer between windings but was not nearly as good as the fusee, its only real advantage being that the works could be more compact. Engraved and gilt cylindrical brass cases, with an hour hand on top and steel and iron works within, are typical of early models. ■ By the end of the 1500s, spring clocks had increased in size and greatly in variety—round, dome-shaped, hexagonal, book-shaped, tower-shaped clocks reflected contemporary architecture, usually

Cutaway of typical tower clock of the 19th century. The pendulums of these clocks were often as long as 13 feet

Gothic in Germany and Renaissance in England and France. Many designs were purely fanciful, reflecting the maker's whimsy: crucifixion scenes, chariots, animals real and mythological. Although the parts were made by specialists, the clock- or watchmaker—before he was accepted by his guild as a master and permitted to keep apprentices—had to build an entire timepiece, from raw metal. ■ The masterpiece was no ordinary timeteller, especially in Nuremberg, but an "organism" proving its maker's experience and skill. One "thesis" by a mid-17th-century Nuremberg clockmaker offered such basic information as hour, quarter-hour, minute, date, German and Italian hours and their strikes, and also the length of daylight in all latitudes, signs of the zodiac, positions of the sun, moon, and planets, and seasonal aspects of the sky. This clock probably cost what a fairly large private aircraft would

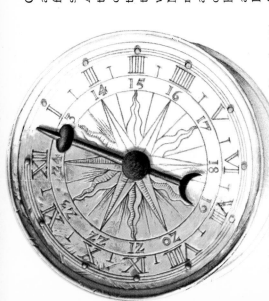

Spring clocks were plain at first, like this early, 16th-century model. Later, as techniques were mastered, they became very elaborate

22

today. There were even clocks capable of spraying perfumes hourly and others were reported to release singing birds to the accompaniment of hymns from a miniature organ pumped and played by the clock's works. Smaller, watch-sized versions of the early 16th-century spring clocks were made at the same time. ■ Peter Henlein, the traditional "inventor" of the watch, probably made his first model (c. 1510) in cylindrical shape, but he was also supposed to have made watches in the form of musk balls, the pierced, engraved, and gilt containers filled with scents and spices worn around the neck by the fashionable and fastidious. The unjustly famous "Nuremberg egg" is a purely mythical watch probably derived from confusing the German

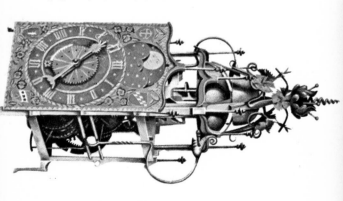

Most early house clocks were Gothic in style, like this 1570 model. All used practically the same escapement as the cathedral clocks

Detail of bell hammers

Detail of the XII

23

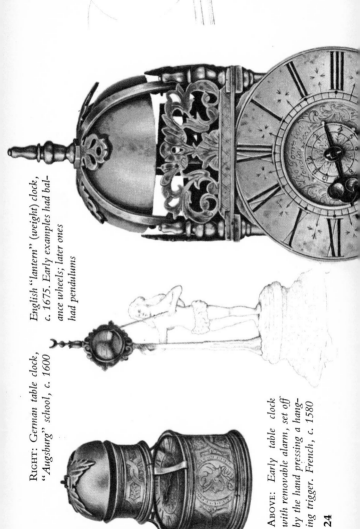

RIGHT: German table clock, "Augsburg" school, c. 1600

English "lantern" (weight) clock, c. 1675. Early examples had balance wheels; later ones had pendulums

ABOVE: Early table clock with removable alarm, set off by the hand pressing a hanging trigger. French, c. 1580

24

Austrian "roller" clock, c. 1665. This clock acts as its own driving weight, the works being driven as it rolls slowly down the ramp. The hour hand remains upright. Reproductions of this clock are made today. The two "falling ball" clocks inside the back cover are similar in principle

words meaning "little egg", and "little clock". ■ Most early watches, like clocks, were German. It was not until the 17th century that French makers won supremacy and the English began to establish themselves as future masters. About 1600, balance wheel supports, called cocks, began to be elaborately pierced and engraved. Between 1670 and 1800 the pillars between the plates of the movement became very ornate; shapes derived from ancient Egyptian columns, tulips, and rococo scrolls delighted the winder's eye. The beauty of these early watches compensated for their bad timekeeping—a watch was enjoyed as a jewel to be displayed; early examples were worn round the neck or at the waist. Only later, when pockets became common, did they tend to be carried out of sight.

■ From the late 1500s to the later 1600s, watches were made in the forms of dogs, rabbits, skulls (like the one carried by Mary, Queen of Scots); their movements were also housed in beautifully enamelled or faceted crystal cases and, in the 1700s, were often contained in as many as three highly decorated, nested cases of intricately pierced and engraved gold and silver. Calendar combinations showing hour, date,

25

motions of the sun, moon, and planets, and with striking mechanisms or alarms, were not uncommon; in some watches the night hours, represented by raised studs, could be felt. Some watches included a sundial—a valuable accessory in the days when only the sun "revolved" with any accuracy. ■ Minute hands, prior to 1675, were rare, although Guy Fawkes is supposed to have bought a watch so equipped in order to time the fire train leading to the gunpowder with which his conspirators hoped to blow up the king and parliament in 1605. Mechanical ingenuity had reached summits of skill, but horology as a science hardly existed. ■ By 1675, however, new clocks varied no more than seconds and watches no more than minutes from true time per day. This was due not so much to improved techniques as to two new elements, the pendulum and the hairspring. A swinging pendulum and a vibrating spring

Galileo's plan for a pendulum escapement. Working models have been made from this sketch (made by his son in 1641), but Galileo's clock remained in the experimental stage

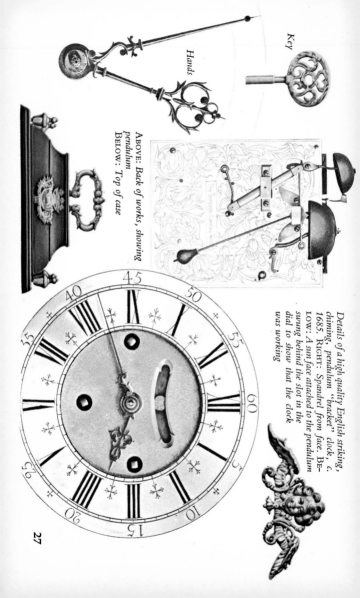

Key

Hands

ABOVE: Back of works, showing pendulum
BELOW: Top of case

Details of a high quality English striking, chiming, pendulum "bracket" clock, c. 1685. RIGHT: Spandrel from face. BELOW: A sun face attached to the pendulum swung behind the slot in the dial to show that the clock was working

27

Watch keys

c. 1600

c. 1800

c. 1800

A. English "4-colour" gold watch, with rubies and sapphires, c. 1800. B. Swiss gilt watch, with pierced cover, c. 1580. C. Swiss enamelled watch and key, with rubies and pearls, c. 1805. RIGHT: Balance-wheel shields or "cocks". D. English, c. 1660. E. French, c. 1740. F. Swiss, c. 1750.

E

F

D

B

C

A

28

pial Swiss
French)
ch with
in and key
green
agreen" or
rkskin-cov-
d case, c.
0

MARCHAND · AVGENEVE

Swiss
watch
and key
c. 1800

Pillars like these separated the front and back plates of the watch movement

29

have, unlike a foliot, practically uniform beats —the shorter their lengths, the faster they beat, and vice versa; an excellent way to "control" the time. About 1493, Leonardo da Vinci sketched a pendulum with portions of clockwork, but this never got farther than his sketchbook. Galileo, "discoverer" of the pendulum, used one to time astronomical observations; a physician friend took the hint and used one to time patients' pulses. Later (1641), blind and ailing, Galileo dictated to his son plans for a pendulum clock. ■ Subsequently, a famous Dutch mathematician, Christiaan Huygens, put a pendulum clock on the market in London in 1657. Advertised to "keep equaller time than any now made", it was an immediate success. Thousands of the old balance-wheel lantern clocks were altered to pendulum, one reason why the originals are so valued by collectors today. ■ The watch's "pendulum" or

LEFT: *French enamelled watch, Louis XIV and Mme. de Maintenon, c. 1685*

RIGHT: *English, c. 1630*

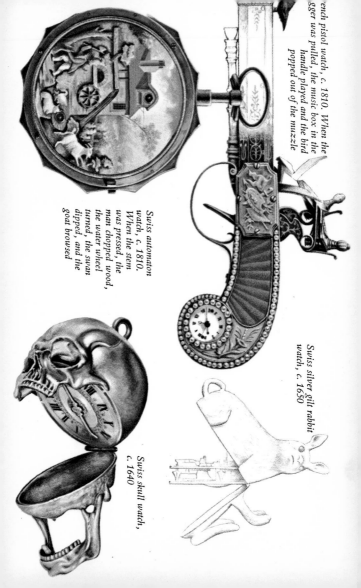

ench pistol watch, c. 1810. When the gger was pulled, the music box in the handle played and the bird popped out of the muzzle

Swiss automaton watch, c. 1810. When the stem was pressed, the man chopped wood, the water wheel turned, the swan dipped, and the goat browsed

Swiss silver gilt rabbit watch, c. 1650

Swiss skull watch, c. 1640

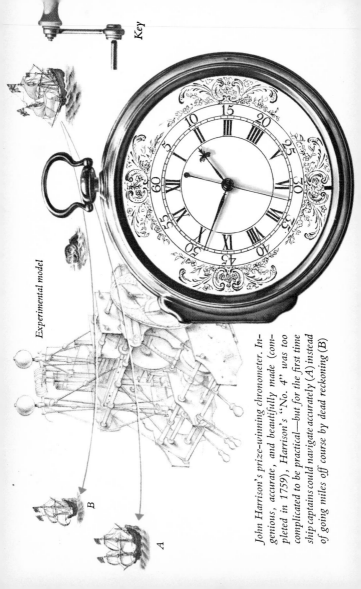

Key

Experimental model

John Harrison's prize-winning chronometer. Ingenious, accurate, and beautifully made (completed in 1759), Harrison's "No. 4" was too complicated to be practical—but for the first time ship captains could navigate accurately (A) instead of going miles off course by dead reckoning (B)

hairspring—the balance beats are controlled by the vibration of its attached hairlike spring—was also invented in practical form by Huygens, although Robert Hooke, the inventor of an improved clock pendulum (1671), contested this bitterly when the model was marketed about 1675. He immediately tried to get a patent from Charles II for his model, but the King, who tested both himself, failed to grant a patent to either. Hooke's models were made by Thomas Tompion—soon to become famous for the beauty and quality of his clocks and watches—but not fast enough for Hooke, who called him in his diary a "slug", "clownish, churlish dog", and "rascal". Keeping accurate time on land was now on its way to people's pockets and houses, but keeping time at sea was still only a dream. ■ If a ship's captain could compare his sun or star time with the corresponding time at his home port, the difference would show him how many degrees (one hour equalling 15 degrees of longitude) and therefore how many miles he had come east or west of his starting longitude. When this was correlated with his latitude, the lucky captain would know exactly where he was—but no one did know until a Yorkshire carpenter, John Harrison, won 20,000 pounds with a watch capable of keeping time well within two minutes after five rough months at sea. This was in 1773—66 years after the prize was first offered by a shipwreck-shocked parliament—a 2,000-man British fleet had "navigated" of course, smashed into the Scilly Islands, and sunk. ■ The late 18th and early 19th centuries saw the perfecting of handmade clocks and watches made up by the maker from semi-finished parts supplied by specialists. A top quality grandfather clock cost the equivalent of a car now; much cheaper "wag on the walls" pendulum clocks could be found in inns and cottages, but there were very few cheap watches—even those of inferior quality were fairly expensive and often forged with the signature of a famous maker. ■ American makers achieved their own clockmaking styles only towards the end of the 18th century. The early makers mostly followed English styles, and had to make everything by hand. Consequently, they used anything they could lay their hands on; dials were sometimes made from pewter plates and hands from old spoons. The much cheaper wood works—fulfilling the clocks-in-quantity ambitions particularly characteristic of the Connecticut makers—did not become profitable until the late 1700s. The first cheap brass clocks were not produced until the 1840s, in Connecticut. ■ The 18th century was a century of glory for English makers, who capitalized on four momentous

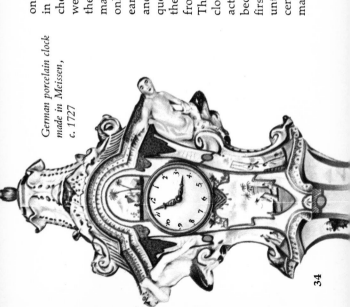

German porcelain clock made in Meissen, c. 1727

34

inventions—Robert Hooke's anchor pendulum; the hairspring; the ship's chronometer; and the lever escapement, invented about 1759 (although unexploited until the early 19th century, this is, with minor changes, almost universally used today). The old verge and crown escape wheel, strong, simple, and understood by all makers since its use in early clocks, continued in use, especially in watches, until about 1800. French makers of the 18th century, especially Julien Le Roy and Jean-Antoine Lépine, were beginning to use the cylinder escapement, practically perfected by "Honest George" Graham in 1725, in the thinner watches then coming into vogue. The pendulum had been almost perfected but the hairspring was not fully understood until the last half of the 19th century. Harrison had compensated—on the hairspring—for temperature troubles (cold speeds, heat slows) in his unique chronometers,

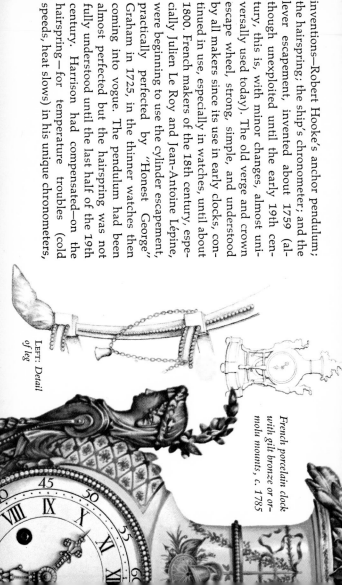

LEFT: Detail
of leg

French porcelain clock
with gilt bronze or or-
molu mounts, c. 1785

RIGHT: *A clock operated by hydrogen, c. 1835. Gas pressure kept weights wound*

ABOVE: *English night or "magic lantern" clock, c. 1810. A lamp and a lens on the inside projected the time on the wall*

but watches and chronometers for the general market required a simpler solution. Pierre Le Roy, son of the famous Julien, left the hairspring alone and (about 1766) concentrated on the balance wheel—causing its self-adjusting rim to cancel out the disturbing effects of temperature changes. ■ The main lines of watch evolution converged on thinness, keylessness, simplicity, and the perfection of both cheap and expensive types of lever escapement. There were many styles, however: musical and striking watches; calendar and astronomical types; alarm (one set in a ring pricked the wearer instead of ringing); automaton, most showing tiny figures striking bells (or even making love); and varieties of second and split-second counters. ■ Although American makers pioneered the mass-produced clock, it was the Swiss who (often using similar techniques) did the same thing successfully for watches.

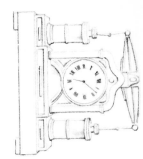

Clocks of the steam age, later 19th century. Mock flywheels, walking beams, governors, and piston rods (driven by a separate spring) moved on the hour—a delight to the steam enthusiast's heart. Thermometers, barometers, hygrometers lent usefulness to novelty

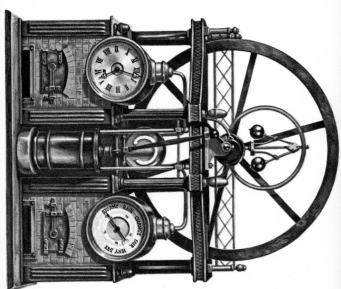

Shapes, styles, and sizes of clocks. FAR LEFT: American "acorn" or "wasp waist", c. 1850, an 8-day pendulum clock. LEFT: Simon Willard banjo clock, c. 1810. ABOVE: Eli Terry shelf clock, c. 1817. RIGHT: A Louis XV "grandfather" clock with inlaid woods, gilt bronze, and enamelled dial. This rococo clock was "high style" around 1745. The dial included sundial time and a perpetual calendar

Machine techniques were already in use by the early 19th century, but they were often trade secrets jealously guarded even from the man and wife teams to whom much of the work was still "farmed out". Mass production and other attempts to "cheapen the trade" were opposed at first–especially by English makers who still turned out the hand-finished and expensive watches. But their days of influence were past–the increasing urban population presented a market not to be ignored, although it was until English watch-making became almost extinct. ■ In 1867 George Roskopf, a Swiss, began to market successfully a mass-produced watch. Still out of the range of many pockets, it was soon carried in more of them than any other maker's. All frills were eliminated; the dial was printed paper and the hands were set, like a clock, with the finger. Roskopf's watches, to the surprise of the industry, actually won a bronze medal at the 1868 Paris Exposition. The day of the cheap watch had officially begun. ■ In the U.S., there were many attempts to establish a watch industry during the 19th century, but most of them were abortive. Probably the first American watches

39

FAR LEFT: *Astronomical and striking watch by Patek, Philippe; 1932. The back dial shows sunrise, sunset, sundial time, sidereal or star time, and constellations. This is probably the most complicated "pocket" watch ever made*

ABOVE: *Dia... with Turkish numerals*
LEFT: *Swiss about 1800*

produced in quantity were made by an itinerant preacher, Luther Goddard of Massachusetts, beginning about 1809. The first financially successful inexpensive American watch was marketed in 1880 by the Waterbury Watch Co. The whole movement revolved in 24 hours; the spring was almost nine feet long and needed a great deal of sore-fingered winding. ■ The versatile maker of horology's golden age has today been replaced by versatile machines. The wrist watch monopolizes design today; no other timekeeper is subject to so many hazards, and these—moisture, dust, shock, magnetism, and temperature changes—have never before been concentrated on so small a machine. Moisture and dust are best resisted by the carefully fitted and gasketed "waterproof" case. Automatic winding, tried sporadically during the 1700s, further reduces the chances of dirt intake around an otherwise much-fingered winder. Jewelled bearings—known for their smooth-running and wear-resisting properties since the early 1700s—can be spring-suspended to resist all but the heavier jars. Magnetism, which can stop a watch, temperature effects, and spring breaking can be practically ruled out by using special alloys. All the approximately 125 parts are shaped by automatic machines and assembled by semi-skilled labour. Only the higher quality watches enjoy hand retouching and only the craftsmen-managers and designers know how to build a complete watch. It is still possible to order an individual watch, but most makers' mottoes might as well be: "When minutes mean money, conformity counts." ■ Electric clocks reach back, at least on paper, into the late 1700s. But the beginning of practical electric clockmanship dates from the 1840s when electricity was run through electromagnets on the pendulum of a clock designed by Alexander Bain of Edinburgh. The pendulum drove the clock—a reversal of the usual practice. Other clocks in the same circuit could now, for the first time in history, be synchronized with a "master clock"—something beyond even the imperial powers of the amateur-horologist and Holy Roman Emperor Charles V, who could well complain in the 1550s: "How much blood I have shed to make men think alike and I cannot even make two clocks agree". But only in the 1920's, on the introduction of dependable alternating current, did electric clocks become popular; "moderns" felt them obligatory. The most familiar type today is dependent on the steadiness of the power station's generators—when the alternations are off, all the clocks along the line will show the same error. Battery wrist watches use two systems: electromagnets drive the watch by acting on the balance wheel, again a reversal of the usual, or by buzzing a tiny tuning fork whose vibrations drive the works. Battery clocks have made a comeback. "Solar" clocks are "wound" by sunlight—tiny storage batteries are recharged by photoelectric cells mounted on the case. ■ Since 1948, when the National Bureau of Standards built the first practical atomic clock, the stars have been in danger of becoming obsolete. Previously, the acme of accuracy, almost equalling the earth, had been the quartz crystal electronic clock. But atomic vibrations are more regular than even the earth's revolutions—so much so that in 1966 an international committee may declare atomic timekeeping the standard. In the Bureau of Standards clock, twice as accurate a timekeeper as the earth, the vibration of nitrogen atoms in ammonia acts as the "escapement". An improved type will not vary more than one second in a thousand years

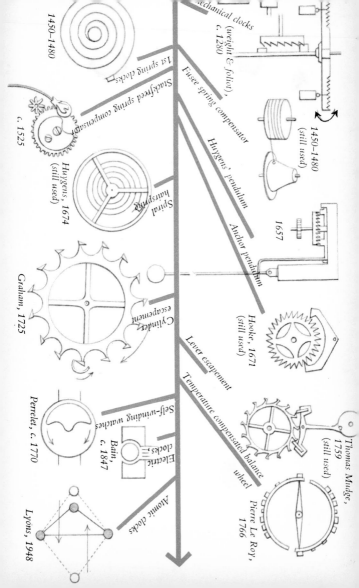

Mechanical clocks (weight & foliot), c. 1280

1450-1480

1450-1480 (still used)

1st spring clocks

Fusee spring compensator

Stackfeed spring compensator

c. 1525

Huygens' pendulum

Huygens, 1674 (still used)

Spiral hairspring

1657

Anchor pendulum

Hooke, 1671 (still used)

Graham, 1725

Cylinder escapement

Lever escapement

Thomas Mudge, 1759 (still used)

Temperature compensated balance wheel

Self-winding watches

Perrelet, c. 1770

Electric clocks

Bain, c. 1847

Pierre Le Roy, 1766

Atomic clocks

Lyons, 1948

and this phenomenal exactness is surpassed by one using cesium atoms. The inventor calculated that had his clock been started at Christ's birth, it would now be no more than one-half second off. And there is talk now of a sub-atomic or nuclear clock! None of these clocks can be considered mantel-piece models. The cesium-type weighs over four hundred-weight and costs £180,000. One may well ask to what end? A fractional second error in rocket timing could, if uncor-rected, mean thousands of solar-system miles off course. If we ever achieve interstellar travel, an uncorrected miss like this could be light-years wide. Even now super-accurate timekeeping is essential on earth. Ammonia and cesium clocks are used to regulate broadcasting frequencies, radio naviga-tion systems, long-range miltary rockets, satellite tracking, and space probes. Spacecraft clocks, as Einstein predicted, will run at different rates—relativity cannot be compensated out! There will be no John Harrison to show true time to Venus; timekeepers travelling in space (and time?) will pose unearthly problems.

"Accutron" electric wrist watch, powered by a miniature cell. A tiny tuning fork acts as the escapement

INDEX

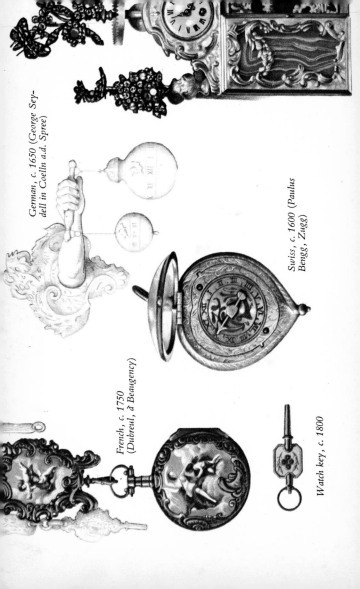

German, c. 1650 (George Sey-dell in Coelln a.d. Spree)

Swiss, c. 1600 (Paulus Bengg, Zugg)

French, c. 1750 (Dubreul, à Beaugency)

Watch key, c. 1800